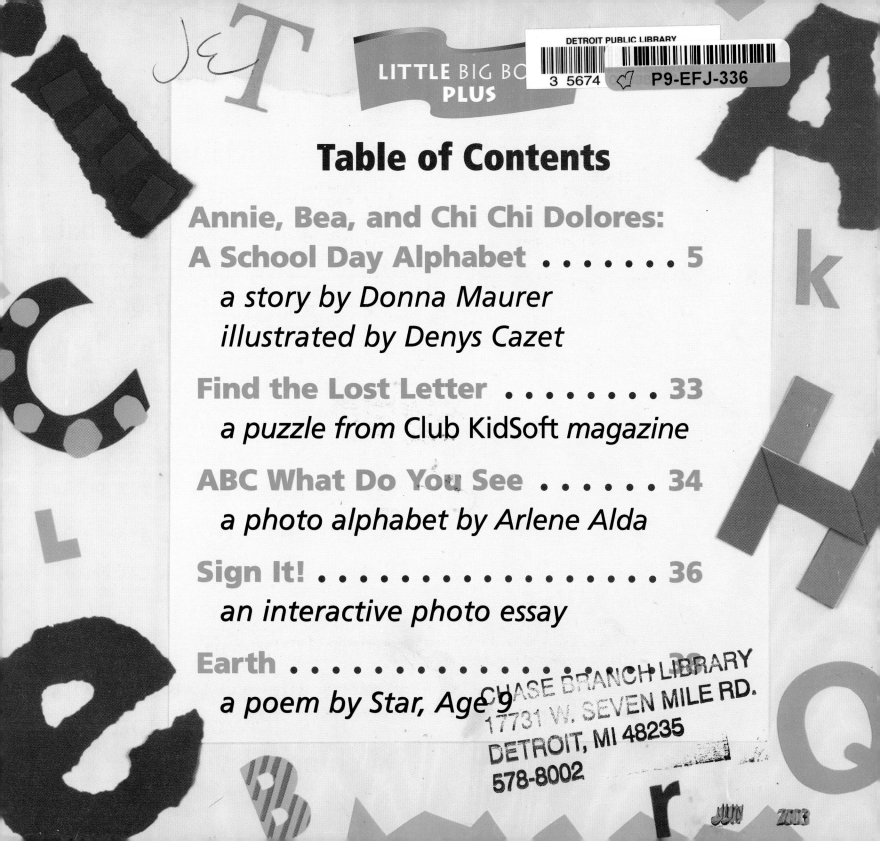

LITTLE BIG BOOK
PLUS

Table of Contents

Meet Donna Maurer

Donna Maurer was a first grade teacher for seven years. She says that many funny things happen in school. Thinking about some of them helped her get ideas for *Annie, Bea, and Chi Chi Dolores.*

Meet Denys Cazet

Children often ask Denys Cazet the secret to drawing. He says, "You start when you are very young, and you never stop." He likes drawing more than watching television!

Annie, Bea, and Chi Chi Dolores

A SCHOOL DAY ALPHABET

by Donna Maurer   pictures by Denys Cazet

HOUGHTON MIFFLIN COMPANY

BOSTON

ATLANTA   DALLAS   GENEVA, ILLINOIS   PALO ALTO   PRINCETON

Acknowledgments

For each of the selections listed below, grateful acknowledgment is made for permission to excerpt and/or reprint original or copyrighted material, as follows:

Text

1 *Annie, Bea, and Chi Chi Dolores,* by Donna Maurer, illustrated by Denys Cazet. Text copyright © 1993 by Donna Maurer. Illustrations copyright © 1993 by Denys Cazet. Reprinted by permission of Orchard Books. **33** "Find the Lost Letter," from Winter 1993 *Club Kidsoft* magazine. Copyright © 1993 by KidSoft, Inc. Reprinted by permission. **34** "What Do You See?" adapted from *Arlene Alda's ABC What Do You See?* by Arlene Alda. Copyright © 1981, 1993 by Arlene Alda. Reprinted by permission of Tricycle Press. **36** "Sign Language," from *Handsigns,* by Kathleen Fain. Copyright © 1993 by Kathleen Fain. Reprinted by permission of Chronicle Books, San Francisco **38** "Earth," by Star Trudell from *Women of the Native Struggle,* by Ronnie Farley. Copyright © 1993 by Ronnie Farley. Reprinted by permission of John Trudell for the author.

Illustrations

38 Darius Detwiler.

Photography

i Banta Digital Group. **ii** Courtesy of Donna Maurer/Orchard Books (t); courtesy of Denys Cazet/Orchard Books (b); Tony Scarpetta (picture frames, background). **33** Tony Scarpetta. **36–37** Tracey Wheeler.

Houghton Mifflin Edition, 1997
Copyright © 1997 by Houghton Mifflin Company. All rights reserved.

Printed in the U.S.A.

ISBN 0-395-80430-2

123456789-B-98 97 96

For my parents,

Sylvester and Virginia Maurer

—D.M.

A a
all aboard

B b
buddies

C c
counting

D d
drawing

E e   erasing

F f follow the leader

G g
giggling

H h
hopping

I i
icky

15

J j jumping rope

K k kicking a ball

16

L l   lining up

17

M m making music

N n   noisy

O o

oops . . .

P p

painting

Q q
quiet

R r
running races

S s   snack time

T t
tickling

U u
untangling

V v
vamoose

W w
whispering

X x

x-ing

29

Y y   yawning

Z z

zip

Find the
Lost Letter

LITTLE BIG BOOK PLUS

The alphabet has 26 letters. But there are only 25 letters here. Which letter is lost?

33

ABC **What Do _You_ See?**

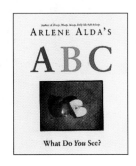

The alphabet is everywhere!
Just look at these pictures.

Now look around your classroom.
What letters can you find?

A

G

H

I

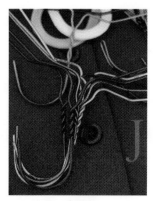

J

K

Q

R

S

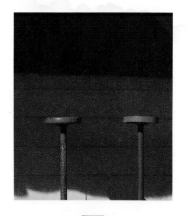

T

U

34

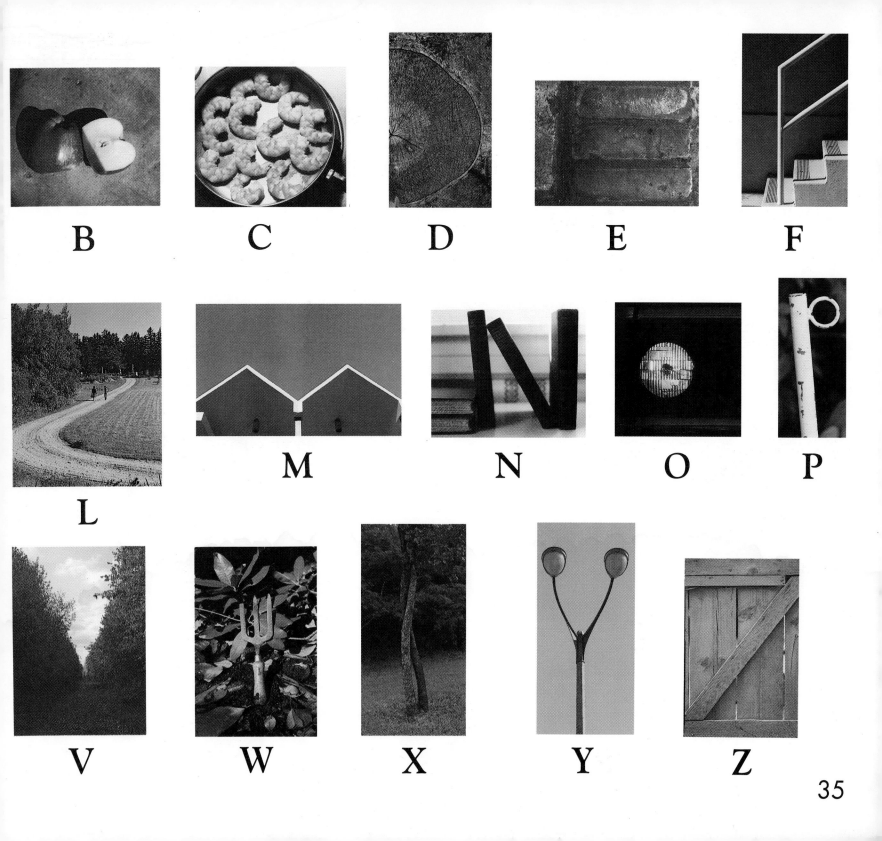

B

C

D

E

F

L

M

N

O

P

V

W

X

Y

Z

35

Aa  Bb  Cc  Dd  Ee  Ff  Gg

Sign It!

These children are *signing* – using their fingers to spell. What names are they signing?

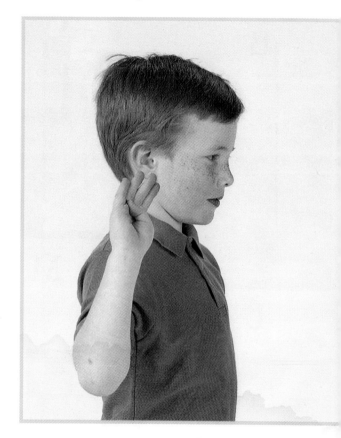

Oo  Pp  Qq  Rr  Ss  Tt

Hh   Ii   Jj   Kk   Ll   Mm   Nn

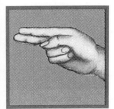  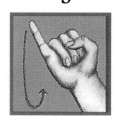   

Can you spell your name
with hand signs? Try it!

Uu   Vv   Ww   Xx   Yy   Zz

     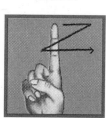

Earth

E is for Earth
A is for Animals
R is for Respect
T is for Trees
H is for Home — what the Earth is.

by Star, Age 9
Lac La Ronge Band Treaty Cree
Saskatchewan
Canada